The First Day

My name is Esther and I'm 11 years old. After going to a private primary school, I'm now in Year 7 at a free-but-posh secondary school in the centre of Paris.

This is me outside my new school in "okay, you're in the big time now" mode

Belly button showing

In fact, I was supposed to go to a school near where we live, the one my brother goes to.

But it's a ZPEP, a violent place where girls are hassled by stupid boys like him

Yo, I just let one rip for you

Can you smell it?

Esther, you smell that?

...exam ...hic ...ly dad

I'm a good student and I'm pretty so I think that the school is lucky to have me

Just kidding, yo!

I say that because the kids in my class are really ugly (not that I care, it's just interesting to observe).

This one, for example, has dark fuzzy hair on her top lip and between her eyebrows, but she seems happy

She's wearing "I'm so fashionable" Stan Smith trainers

This boy looks like a girl. Long hair, high-pitched voice... And he smells like damp laundry...

I sat behind him in one class and had his stink in my nostrils all day long

This one looks like a CHICK (a baby chicken, I mean, not a girl).

Cute and sweet but, you know, I could never be "friends" with that

Then there are some boys from Porchgull or something. Their mums are caretakers for apartment buildings.

They have almost-footballer hair

Always together

There's only one boy I think is handsome. His name is Louis. Check out his magnificent jawline and how well it goes with his neck!

Black curly hair

Looks open to life

Perfectly straight nose

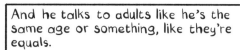

And he talks to adults like he's the same age or something, like they're equals.

Have you conferred with the other teachers to limit the number of books we have to carry around? So our bags are less heavy?

Good idea!

Ah, that's a shame.

Um, no, I haven't.

Yep, the teachers are ANCIENT!

I was hanging around in the courtyard the other day in "I have a feeling I'm not going to have any friends this year" mode, and he came over to TALK to me!

Hi there, I'm Louis... I hope I'm not disturbing you?

I, uh, no...

He really talks like an adult, right?

I had a question for you... it's probably stupid of me, but... are you the one who plays SOLINE LEPIC in "Fais pas ci, fais pas ça"?

N... No! I...

Wow, you look just like her!

"Fais pas ci, fais pas ça" is a funny TV show about families, and Soline Lepic is one of the characters and she's beautiful.

This is her

Gorgeous brunette

Deep, confident voice

Playful, flirtatious look

Am I really like her?

THIS BOY IS PERFECT (LOL)

(Based on a true story told by Esther A, who is 11 years old)

Riad Sattouf

Gods

This year, in history, we're studying the Greeks.

This is me pretending to be interested

The Greeks were polytheistic. Who knows what that means?

Polytheism means having lots of different gods. It's a really good idea.

Look at them all!

It's much better than what we have now, where there's just one boy-god...

Like a dictator who knows everything...

I'm in charge of the universe

Posing in "I'm the best" mode

When there's only one god, I feel alone and abandoned. Because if he has to do everything on his own, he's bound to be overworked...

Dear God, please cancel tomorrow's English test, I beg you, Lord

How many people are asking him stuff like that, all at the same time?

So I'm left with the impression that he doesn't do anything.

Sorry, I was busy, I forgot

You have one hour

But the Greeks had a whole team of gods, each taking care of different things, and some of them were GIRLS (they're called goddesses).

Persephone (goddess of spring)

Demeter (goddess of harvests)

Tyche (goddess of luck)

Atë (goddess of mistakes)

I think it's a really good idea to have a goddess exclusively for love, for example: Aphrodite.

A super-hot goddess in a bikini who devotes her life to matters of the heart

Then there were some stupid, pointless gods like Apollo, the god of cool dudes...

Look, he's half naked!

Well, I'm sure there are SOME people who look like that (yeah, right)

It takes all sorts! (LOL)

My favourite goddess is Athena. I love her. She's the goddess of war but also (less famously) wisdom.

I think about her a lot

She's a good role model for us women, I think

The story of her birth is hilarious. One day, Zeus – the king of gods – had a terrible headache, so he asked Hephaestus (the god of metal and weapons) to smash him over the head with an axe (to take the pain away LOL).

Hit me right here...

Okay, boss

And the big lump DID IT.

Better now, boss?

Just then, Athena burst out of Zeus's head wearing armour, in "worship me" mode!

YAAAAAH!

(Based on a true story told by Esther A, who is 11 years old)

Riad Sattouf

4

Riad Sattouf

ESTHER'S NOTEBOOKS

Tales from my 12-year-old life

Just to reassure you...

...I'm one of the popular girls

Translated from the French by Sam Taylor

PUSHKIN PRESS

The New Goddesses

I don't believe in God, but ever since we started studying the Greeks, I've become interested in gods.

This is me as Athena (I adore her)

I think it's an excellent idea to have lots of gods for different things instead of just one god for everything.

I am Everything!

I control Every-thing!

I know Every-thing!

Not really likely, is it?

I think we should replace our single-boy-god with some more modern goddesses.

Here are some that I invented!

They were born from my head (LOL)

Wify
Goddess of electronic devices and the internet

Knows all secret codes

Fixes smartphones

Good signal strength

Boyzia
Goddess of relationships with boys

Strong and fights like a boy

Protects weaker girls

Dancy
Goddess of bendiness and sport

You lose weight when you pray to her

Smarta
Goddess of nerds and school

Helps you pass or cancel tests

Aids memory

Athena
Goddess of war and wisdom

Bad-girl-style camouflage

I'm keeping her but modernizing her appearance

Oceania
Goddess of oceans and nature

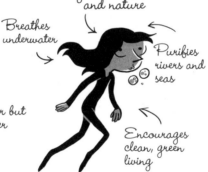

Breathes underwater

Purifies rivers and seas

Encourages clean, green living

Workina
Goddess of employment

Helps you find a job when you're older

The Great Mother
Goddess of mums

Always surrounded by levitating babies

Nocturna
Goddess of peaceful sleep and sweet dreams

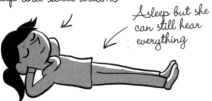

Asleep but she can still hear everything

Uglia
Goddess of people with challenging appearances

Dries their tears and helps them succeed

Goddess of humour

Esther
Goddess of popular people

Just kidding, of course!

(Based on a true story told by Esther A, who is 11 years old)

Riad Sattouf

Trump

In the mornings, my dad wakes my brother and me so we won't be late for school (my mum has already left for work). He's usually in a good mood.

But not this morning → SOMETHING TERRIBLE'S HAPPENED!

This is me

← Only one eye open

TRUMP HAS BEEN ELECTED PRESIDENT!

YO, nice one, Donald

My brother the idiot

WHAT? SERIOUSLY?

I must admit I didn't know much about him (I'm not into politics, sorry) but my dad talked about Trump all the time because he was so afraid he'd become president.

and it was around 11 o'clock that Trump moved so far ahead of Clinton that his victory became indisputable

OH GOD ooooooh fucking hell!

Why do you care so much yo?

And then at school everybody was in "Trump is the devil" mode, it was really funny.

IS THERE ANYONE HERE WHO LIKES TRUMP? TELL ME NOW SO I CAN NEVER SPEAK TO YOU AGAIN!

This Year 8 girl actually shouted that in the courtyard!

And then everybody in class was talking about it and the teacher told off one boy who made a joke about Trump being a duck (his first name is Donald, like the Disney character).

IT WAS A JOKE, SIR, I DON'T LIKE TRUMP

Hmph

Perhaps, but mediocre puns add nothing to the debate.

The President of America is the most powerful leader in the world (I don't know why, apparently that's just how it is), and the Americans just had an election to decide who would take over from Obama, a nice Renoi (that's what us kids call Black people).

The people had to choose between Clinton...

... and Trump

← I don't know who she is

Everybody thought Clinton was going to win. Everybody. And then, at the last second, Trump was elected.

Those Americans...

They chose a Renoi to be president, so why not let a woman try? Anyway...

Trump wants to DESTROY his enemies. He SAYS he's racist (nobody else dares say it), he HATES the Renois, the Rebeus (what us kids call Arab people) and the Noiches (Chinese people). But apparently France is on his list of friends (lucky us).

He looks crazy

I wouldn't like to be his enemy

You know the weirdest thing though? Donald Trump used to be POLYGAMOUS!

That means he had sex with lots of women he didn't love!

← Un-be-liev-able

← Although it's normal too, I guess: he's a boy

I think everybody's overreacting though. I saw Trump's wife and she seems like a good person. I mean, she used to be a model, and she's 25 while he's 80, so it's obvious that she's manipulating him.

She's, like, a million times too pretty for him

I like her hairstyle

→ Everything in harmony

Straight, thin nose →

Nicely shaped mouth

← Calm and composed

I have a feeling she'll be the one actually running things. What do you think?

Don't worry, Dad. It'll be okay, I'm sure of it.

I hope so, sweetie...

I could tell straight away that my words had soothed him.

(Based on a true story told by Esther A, who is 11 years old)

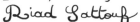

The Tutorial

I've had a few zits recently (very annoying).

This is me rummaging through my mum's make-up bag

Make-up means hiding imperfections or enhancing facial features with special products made for that purpose.

"Concealer"... Hmm, interesting...

My mum hardly ever wears make-up but she has loads of products that I like to try. Let me show you...

Concealer is a sort of undercoat that hides zits and dark rings

You apply generously then spread it around with the stick

Then you get some foundation and you smear it all over your face.

It's a thick, pink-beige paste that you spread from the centre to the outside

It always makes my face look more tanned than my neck (although with a turtleneck sweater I doubt anyone can tell).

Next, you put on some powder to take the shine off and now I look like I've just come back from my holidays (LOL).

COUGH!

Then you can use some mascara (this black stuff that thickens your eyelashes and makes you look all sultry).

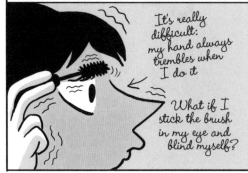

It's really difficult: my hand always trembles when I do it

What if I stick the brush in my eye and blind myself?

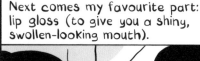

Next comes my favourite part: lip gloss (to give you a shiny, swollen-looking mouth).

Sensuality

When I see myself like that, I think I look about 25-30 years old.

Grown woman

FUCK ME THAT'S GROSS YO

Don't move

VLAK

OWW

I like hurting my brother

(Based on a true story told by Esther A, who is 11 years old)

Riad Sattouf

Violence

I'm in Year 7 at a posh school in the centre of Paris. I'm going to change its real name and call it the "ROYAL School" to protect my privacy (and also because I think it's funny).

This is me in "surprise test" mode

To get in, I had to pass a very difficult test because the school I was supposed to go to, near where I live, was full of violence towards girls, and that worried my dad.

Well, God knows what the other school is like because there's loads of violence towards girls at the Royal School

You have five minutes left

Let me tell you what happened to me. There are three Year 9 boys who are all really big and they hang out together in the yard and they're always picking on Year 7 kids.

They talk like rappers and dress like my brother →
Sneering
Hoodie
Tracksuit bottoms
Shark trainers ↗

At the cafeteria, they shake down desserts from other boys. They make it sound like a joke because if not they'd get in trouble.

GIMME THAT YOGHURT, YOU LITTLE QUEER
HAHA
I'M JUST KIDDING ...
NOT!
HA HA

Afterwards, in the courtyard, they pretend to be friends with boys from my class...

HEY THERE, MATE!
MAAATE
Hello
HOW ARE YOU DOING, MATE?

... and then they grab them from behind and it almost always ends up in a fight.

A very one-sided fight
HA HA

The other day, I'd had enough of this.

HEY, STOP THAT NOW!
Nobody ever intervenes →
?

As soon as I said that, this crowd gathered round us.

Whadja say? Apologize to your master.
← Those were his words
NO!

CLAK

WOOOOOOOOH!

WOOOO!

It wasn't a really hard slap but it still knocked my head sideways. I looked around at the people laughing and one of them was THE BOY THAT I'D DEFENDED!

They were beating him up, like, thirty seconds before this! How stupid is he?

Hee hee

So I realized that it's not a place that breeds violence... IT'S BOYS.

If there are any boys reading this page, I have a question for you: WHY DO YOU LIKE VIOLENCE?

ANSWER ME.

(Based on a true story told by Esther A, who is 11 years old)

Riad Sattouf

Smartphones

I thought life in secondary school would be more difficult (in terms of the classes, making friends and new ways of behaving).

This is me and Eva (my new best friend, who I really look up to) monitoring the monitors

Okay, he's gone

All RIGHT! Let's look at Facebook...

My life was turned upside down this week. Let me explain...

Use of mobile phones is banned at my school since three hoodie boys showed some "shocking" pictures to Year 7 kids.

Typical violent, brainless Year 9 boys

Trying to look like warriors or something

But when the father of a Year 7 kid complained, the three boys denied it and there was no proof so they weren't punished... so the whole school has been punished instead. Mobile phones have been banned! (Thanks a lot, you three morons.)

You get a two-day suspension if you're caught with a phone, but we're risking it anyway

All clear

Everybody at my school has a smartphone (with a touch screen and all that).

Except me – I have a Nokia, which is, like, just a phone...

... although it does have a few games

The only smartphones anyone respects here are iPhones. And the one everybody dreams of having is the iPhone 5S (more than the 6 or 7, weirdly).

Yeah, Dad, where are you?

The ones who have them are popular

Yep, even this ugly girl with the monobrow!

She Facetimes her dad when school is over so everybody will say "Whoa, a 5S..."

I was so ashamed of my Nokia that I would hide it like this when I called my dad after school.

My long hair concealed my shame

Yeah, where are you, Dad?

And then last week, Eva changed my life. That girl is a genius, I swear.

You poor thing... Let me borrow your phone.

She grabbed my Nokia and did this.

SPLUGH

Now see what happens

Result: it still worked, but nobody could hear me when I spoke!

Why doesn't it work any more?

I acted like nothing had happened

My dad was annoyed, but then he went to his room, and came back with his old iPhone 3... and GAVE IT TO ME!

Here, there's no internet but it works!

AND NOW I HAVE AN IPHONE!

And I can even go on the internet because Eva lets me share her network

I can't believe it!

Eva, my saviour!

Yessss!

(Based on a true story told by Esther A, who is 11 years old)

Riad Sattouf

The Magic of Christmas

I'm a "list" girl. I write lists all the time. They make life clear and simple. For example, here's my list of everything I love about Christmas.

This is me in the street, thinking about my list

1. The Christmas tree, of course, and the decorations. I love string lights and the reflections on the baubles and the smell of the fir tree.

Our tree always leans to the side but I still love it

2. My 1-year-old brother Gaetan's face when he looks at the tree.

My little brother in "the most beautiful thing I've ever seen" mode

3. Writing to Father Christmas instead of doing homework.

"Dear Father Christmas, I'd like an iPhone 7 because my iPhone 3 is rubbish. No, just kidding, I know it's too expensive. Um, anything would be great."

4. TV ads for toys – you never see them at any other time of year.

Hey, a toy that makes REAL cakes! WOW!

Smoby Smoby Chef! Mummy we love cakes! Yeaaahh! There are loads of recipes, cool gadgets, and cupcakes...

5. Decorations in the street.

Beautiful "fairy-tale" atmosphere

6. Watching "Santa Claus Is a Stinker" with my dad, who complains he's seen it too many times but always laughs at it.

HAHAHA

IT'S SO FUNNY!

It's Klug, rolled under the armpits

7. All the different chocolates you can only get at Christmas.

Papillotes (delicious)

Kinder Father Christmases (yum)

Lindt Pyrénéens (melt in the mouth!)

Idea: why not sell them all year round?

8. Trying to guess from the shapes of the presents hidden in my parents' cupboard whether they've got us what we wanted.

GAASP! But... is it... an iPhone?

I DAREN'T BELIEVE IT !

9. Criticizing what my parents eat on Christmas Eve.

It's funny seeing his reaction

But Dad, don't you realize you're eating the sick liver of a DEAD BIRD?

A DEAD BIRD!

10. The Yule log, because the idea of it disgusts me every year (wood as a cake: that's just weird, right?) and yet it tastes amazing.

Yum

11. Opening my presents (I didn't want to put this at number 1 because it seems greedy) and being a bit... well, DISAPPOINTED.

Ooh, the new iPhone! That's great!

Esther, are you happy too? Can I taste your cupcakes?

(Based on a true story told by Esther A, who is 11 years old)

Riad Sattouf

Hamster Years

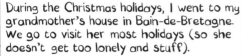

During the Christmas holidays, I went to my grandmother's house in Bain-de-Bretagne. We go to visit her most holidays (so she doesn't get too lonely and stuff).

This is me before I show you something

It's ooooookaaaaaay... shh, sweetheart shh, it's oookaaaay...

So... very carefully, I'd like to introduce you...

Shhhh, it's okay

Please welcome ...

... MANUELA.

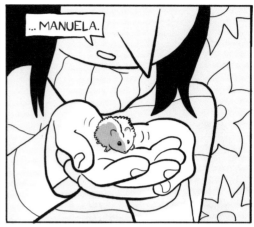

She's a small "sapphire"-coloured Russian hamster that I got for Christmas.

Look at the size of my thumb next to her

Curious little thing

She's called Manuela in tribute to Manuela Diaz, a little girl from "The Voice Kids" who sings like an angel

I wasn't expecting her at all. I hadn't asked for a pet! She was a gift from my grandmother.

A real animal is so much better than your electronic gadgets, you'll see. But it's a big responsibility!

You can tell she's my father's mother – she thinks like him (LOL)

A Russian hamster is a hamster that comes from Russia apparently. It's a quiet little rodent, smaller than a golden hamster but more elegant and less clumsy (IMO).

A golden hamster

Manuela

My sweet

Honestly, which one do you prefer?

Manuela's house
(which I also got as a present)

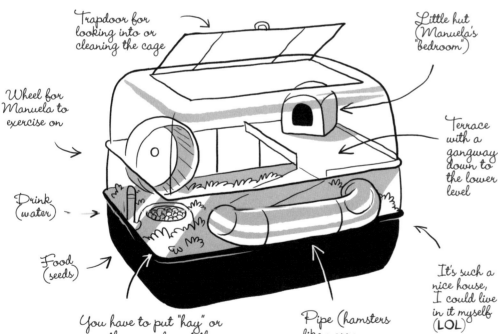

Trapdoor for looking into or cleaning the cage

Little hut (Manuela's "bedroom")

Wheel for Manuela to exercise on

Terrace with a gangway down to the lower level

Drink (water)

Food (seeds)

You have to put "hay" or something similar at the bottom of the cage because hamsters are burrowers (they like to dig)

Pipe (hamsters like narrow tunnels and stuff, don't ask me why)

It's such a nice house, I could live in it myself (LOL)

Hamsters live about 2 years apparently. Manuela is 2 months old, which is about 20 in human years.

Manuela, you were born last October and you're already a young woman...

I calculated how old I would be in hamster years, and the answer was 408.

I'm a 408-year-old hamster!

Like, whoooa

(Based on a true story told by Esther A, who is 11 years old)

Riad Sattouf

11

The Gay Teacher

I'm not a problem student. I mean, I always do my homework even if I don't feel like it, in "I have to do it anyway so why kick up a fuss?" mode.

All riiiight... I've marked your stories! So many good things, genuinely! I am thrilled. Apparently, my dears, you were truly inspired by the story of Ariadne and the Minotaur...

So... the best story of all was by...

Can you guess?

The kids in my class think the French teacher is gay (they call him a "queer" but I think that's insulting).

Everybody hates him because of that. And it's true, he is really annoying with his little expressions and his "touchy-feely" personality.

He, like, totally adores me. It's so embarrassing.

A boy shouldn't say he loves a colour in front of everybody like that... It's girls who are supposed to express their feelings...

Boys should be tough and mysterious.

If boys start acting like girls, what will girls have left?

A boy is a boy and a girl is a girl. Nobody likes it when the two get mixed up. Well, I don't anyway.

Esther, don't you think it's weird the way the teacher talks to you? Watch yourself because he looks like he wants to RAPE you!

(Based on a true story told by Esther A, who is 11 years old)

Riad Sattouf

12

The Fresh Tune

There's a totally fresh (that means good) tune at the moment that everybody loves. It's the new single by Black M.

Black M is a very good-looking rapper. I didn't used to listen to his stuff because my stupid brother liked it, but actually his new song is really good.

It's called "French Kiss" and it's about... well, I'm not sure but it's definitely not about kissing.

And when he opens it he sees this incredibly beautiful girl (my age, I think).

After that, they drink some Innocent orange juice (that's a brand).

Then they're under a duvet and the girl is making these really beautiful "weird" movements.

In the morning, the girl brings him breakfast and there's another bottle of Innocent orange juice!

And then she's in the bath, dreaming about a rubber duck.

And after that they laugh like crazy in "we're disguised as robots" mode.

And after THAT they do this really impressive "hip-hop" dance (the best kind of dancing in the world but also the hardest) and you understand that they're actually these amazing dancers.

Dad, would it bother you if I had dreadlocks?

When you're 18? Not at all!

My dad is sooo funny

We walked through the fruit juice aisle and I saw a bottle of Innocent. I didn't ask my dad if we could buy some because I knew what he would say LOL.

But it did look really good →

(Based on a true story told by Esther A, who is 11 years old)

Riad Sattouf

13

The Illness

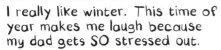

I really like winter. This time of year makes me laugh because my dad gets SO stressed out.

This is me coming home from school in "I'm going to tease him" mode

DAD! GIVE ME A HUG!

ESTHER! WHAT DO WE DO WHEN WE COME IN FROM OUTDOORS?

"We don't wash our hands and we lick our fingers after they've touched the metal poles in the metro"

SCHLRPSSS

ESTHER THAT'S DISGUSTING, YOU...

Just kiddiiing! Look, clean hands!

I used this

Hand sanitizer

My dad is strong and muscular (he doesn't fear anyone) and intelligent (he passed his bac) and sensitive (cries while watching TV sometimes) but he is WAY too scared of germs.

Dad, you're crazy

AHHH, good girl! Hey, let me have some!

Slurrp

He's worried that I'll get a stomach bug, which can make you vomit and/or have diarrhoea... Stomach bugs usually last 2 or 3 days and they're very contagious.

You can catch it by shaking hands

Or from someone breathing

Every time someone with a stomach bug flushes the toilet, a thousand million germs are released

Door handle covered in germs (invisible)

My dad says the French are disgusting because they never wash their hands after going to the toilet.

I must admit none of the girls in my school wash their hands

PSCHHH

He says France is the only country where there are epidemics of stomach bugs. In other countries, everybody washes their hands apparently.

On the train to Brittany, I saw this old woman flush the toilet and leave, but I DIDN'T hear the tap run.

CLAK

SSSHHH

YU-UCK

And she was in first class too (for rich people)

What's funny (although also sad) is that despite all his precautions, my dad is always catching stomach bugs at his gym.

Are you okay, Dad?

Yes, yes... Esther, I'm on the toilet, just leave me in peace

Afterwards, he has to eat potatoes and drink flat Coke and my brother Antoine cruelly mocks him.

You don't wash your hands properly, yo, it's disgusting, ha ha

My poor suffering father

Anyway, we all end up getting it from him.

And it's obvious that he blames himself

So... People of France, please wash your hands

(Based on a true story told by Esther A, who is 11 years old)

Riad Sattouf

The Crime Syndicate

My school is a free school where all the students are from very rich families (correction: all but me).

This is me in the courtyard in "yup, I think it's winter" mode

So anyway, the other day Big Baby (that's my nickname for a boy in my class who looks like a big baby) came to see me and said:

Um, Esther, could you lend me 2 euros?

You can have it back next week I promise

Not so long ago he laughed at me after I'd defended him from these bullies, so I just said, "No, go away."

He went straight to someone else

Excuse me! Can you lend me 2 euros? You'll get it back, I promise

Then Eva (my best friend) came to see me. She was laughing.

Hey, what's going on? All the Year 7 boys are trying to borrow money!

IT WAS, LIKE, REALLY WEIRD.

All the Year 7 boys were asking girls for money

After a while, one of the nerds complained to a monitor.

Sir, he's trying to get money off me!

Then things got out of hand!

At this school there are three thugs in Year 9 who are always getting into trouble

Now don't ask me why, but two Year 10 boys started copying their style and now they are thugs too.

Before, they were like this:

And now they're like this:

And they've become the bosses of the Year 9 thugs. They asked them for money to buy stuff, so the Year 9 thugs asked the Year 7 boys to find them some money.

They were called the "Boyz 4 Crime gang"

You have to write for as 4 because that's how it is on the street (and I must admit I like it)

After Big Baby got in trouble, the headmaster put an end to the gang's activities. But there was no evidence against the thugs, so only the Year 7 kids were punished.

They always get away with it

Very cunning

But apparently Big Baby has received threats. He was the one who tried to snitch on the thugs after someone snitched on him and now they want to kill him.

Now, after school, he hurries to his parents' car

BIG BABY IS 4 IT NOW!!!

(I know it's not funny for him but still)

(Based on a true story told by Esther A, who is 11 years old)

Riad Sattouf

The Life Test

It was my birthday this week and now I'm 12! It's funny because at my school we had the medical visit (it only happens in Year 7 apparently) and it was like I was taking a "life test" or something. Two nurses measured me and stuff while asking me scientific/personal questions ("Do you have any family problems? Have you ever taken drugs? Have you had your period?"). This gave me the idea of making a progress report on myself for a joke (I love talking about myself, I must admit LOL).

Me at 12

Height: 152cm! Not tall, not short, just normal. Need to keep growing (minimum height for a model: 175cm)

Weight: 41kg. Yes, I'm telling you my weight — I'm a modern girl

A bit pigeon-toed (not too badly)

← Hair: thick and luxuriant

Arms: slender and graceful (I like my arms)

Legs: too thin (they make an L with my too-big feet)

Feet: size 34 (and Stan Smiths start at 35, so I have to be patient LMAO)

Nose: straight (thankfully)

Head: leans forward a bit (but I always lift it up, imagining that there's a thread pulling on it — a technique I learned in dance class)

Pretty even from behind (yes, I love myself — well, it's better than hating myself, right?)

My complex: I have some white spots at the edge of my nose

Yeah, you can see I'm pigeon-toed

Nurse's verdict: I am normal

Should I change my hairstyle to celebrate?

Braids? A bit "little girl"

Bob? Too "goody-two-shoes"

Cornrows? Daring — I like it

Pageboy? I love this

Go back to a ponytail?

Oh, and my eyesight is excellent. I took an eye exam and I could see everything

Can you read this? If not, call the doctor!

Now I'm 12, I'll finally be able to watch the film "50 Shades of Grey", a scandalous movie about an all-consuming passion, forbidden to under-12s!

Handsome and tough

Submissive and passionate

(Just kidding — I don't really want to see it LOL)

(Based on a true story told by Esther A, who is 12 years old)

Riad Sattouf

The Review

Did you know that I'm a world-famous celebrity? Okay, that's a slight exaggeration (I'm funny, right?)

This is me feeling pretty pleased about my 19/20 in French, tapping in the code to get into our apartment building

For the past two and a half years I've been telling stories about my life to a cartoonist friend of my dad's and he makes them into books.

A new volume just came out and I read it

To be honest I never read "Esther's Notebooks" in the newspaper where it appears. I always forget, even though my dad gets that paper. I read them in book form instead.

This is what I think of the new one:

It's a very realistic depiction of my life (tastes, hairstyle changes, relationships with friends and lovers)

Although...

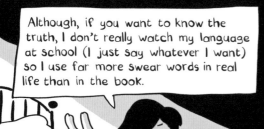

Although, if you want to know the truth, I don't really watch my language at school (I just say whatever I want) so I use far more swear words in real life than in the book.

For example in the first panel of page 21 in that book, it's like this:

My brother Antoine goes to a free (but really violent) school. Thankfully, I escaped it.

This is me with Cassandra trying to avoid Eugenie in the playground

Let's pretend we haven't seen her

Yeah

But in real life, it'd be more like:

My brother Antoine goes to a free (but really violent) school. Thankfully, I escaped it.

This is me with Cassandra trying to avoid Eugenie in the playground

C'mon, we don't give a shit about her

Yeah

Or in panel 2 on page 15:

We each had to take one of our old toys so they could be given to a poor child.

I brought my Cicciobello...

Really? You didn't want to keep it?

It's a doll that talks if you put batteries in it

Pfft, it's a baby toy!

And the truth:

We each had to take one of our old toys so they could be given to a poor child.

I brought my Cicciobello...

Really? You didn't want to keep it?

It's a doll that talks if you put batteries in it

Nah, I don't give a shit about it!

Honestly, everybody says "I don't give a shit". It means "I don't care"

You can also say "I don't give a flying fuck"

I say that a lot.

"I DON'T GIVE A FLYING FUCK"

I know what "fuck" means... It's how babies are made.

But I'm not sure about a flying fuck.

How would that work?

To be honest I never read "Esther's Notebooks" in the newspaper where it appears. I always forget, even though my dad gets that paper. I read them in book form instead.

This is what I think of the new one:

It's a very realistic depiction of my life (tastes, hairstyle changes, relationships with friends and lovers)

Although... I don't really give a shit!

(Based on a true story told by Esther A, who is 12 years old)

Riad Sattouf

Religions

Sorry if you're shocked by this but no, I still don't believe in God or in religions or any magic stuff at all really.

This is me laughing at these subjects

Ha ha "God"! I mean, come on...

It's not a subject that interests me (my favourite subjects are things like "music", "fashion" and "the art of living") but everybody in my school is in "God exists" mode.

These are the religions that I know about:

1. The Estherians. I'm their goddess...

Just kidding

1. The Christians. Their god is called, well, "God", and their lives seem to revolve around that.

Me if I was Christian

Oh how I adore little baby Jesus!

Eugenie, an ex-friend of mine, used to dress like this

You can get cursed in this religion if you disobey Jesus (the Christians' prophet) because he died "for us" or something, but that's all I know.

You have to pray like this if you're a Christian, with a wooden cross round your neck

Forgive me, Lord

Yeah, this type of cross

2. The Jews. Their god is Yahweh, and all I know is that they have loads of holidays (good idea) and that they dress in black and wear big hats and have hair hanging down by their ears.

Me if I was Jewish

Yay, a holiday!

I saw this in an old film, "Rabbi Roger" or something

People often think I'm Jewish because apparently Esther is a Jewish name.

Esther! Oh, so you're Feuj

YEAH!

Ah, cool

Actually, NO!

HA HA

I think it's really funny, sorry

---

3. The Muslims. Their god is Allah and that's all I know. Terrorists are often mostly Muslim but that doesn't mean that all TERRORISTS are Muslim.

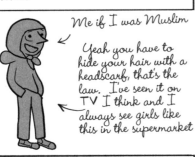

Me if I was Muslim

Yeah you have to hide your hair with a headscarf, that's the law. I've seen it on TV I think and I always see girls like this in the supermarket

Sorry, what I meant was "that doesn't mean that all MUSLIMS are terrorists" (it was a stupid mistake because I don't know anything about it, I'm sorry, please forgive me if I offended anyone).

Sorry again. I am just a child ♥

4. The Buddhists. I don't know the name of their god and I don't know anything about what they do except that they wear red cloths and spend ages meditating.

Me if I was a Buddhist

You have to put your fingers like this

Meditating is staying completely still and calm and living in the present moment intensely and in "no stress" mode.

That's totally me! I'm a natural Buddhist!

(LOL)

So that's all the religions I know. And I find it weird that they all fight each other when they all have the same god. Well, yeah, there's only one god!

Although, as a non-believer, it's probably a bit weird for me to say that...

I'm very tired...

So just ignore everything I said and worship whatever god you like. Let's talk about something else...

I'm going to watch "Une saison au zoo" on France 4.

Girl completely uninterested by the subject of religion (LOL)

(Based on a true story told by Esther A, who is 12 years old)

Riad Sattouf

18

The Candidates

I got really stressed out this week.

This is me listening to my dad in "him talking as usual mode" when suddenly...

If Marine Le Pen is elected, we're moving to Belgium!

On my mother's life that's what he said ("on my mother's life" means I swear". It's the language of the street, yo!)

Apparently we're having an election soon to choose a new French president (I didn't realize because I'm not allowed to watch TV).

The president at the moment is François Hollande →

Fairly okay I think →

So I started taking an interest in politics because I REALLY don't want to live anywhere else.

This is what I know about the presidential candidates

And what I think of their looks

Because that's important.

1. FRANCOIS FILLON

Good-looking for his age (old)

But he's on the right (doesn't like the poor, prefers the rich)

Might go to prison in fact because he gave his wife loads of money and it wasn't allowed (don't ask me why it wasn't allowed)

Chances of becoming president: zero

2. MANUEL VALLS

Not bad, but too skinny

Also on the right I think

I don't know much about him

Apparently has a good chance of winning

3. ALAIN JUPPE

If he had hair, he'd be okay

Hates Fillon (an old feud or something)

Also on the right

Chances of being president: a bit

4. MACRON (I can't remember his first name)

Never seen his face so I can't judge

All I know is he's "in the race"

On the right (yep, him too LOL)

Chances of being elected: unlikely if nobody knows who he is

5. POISSON (I forgot his first name too, but his surname is funny)

Apparently he'd be a dictator (although I could be wrong)

On the left

Chances of becoming president: impossible

"President Fish" (LMAO)

6. BENOIT HAMON

Physically: not my type

BUT

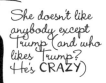

I'd vote for him if I could because he said that if he was elected he'd give money to everybody every month, just to make them happy, you know, and I like that idea

7. MARINE LE PEN

I won't say anything about her looks but I put her in last place so you can guess what I think of her

I don't know if she's left or right but she must be bad because my dad's scared of her

She could also go to prison (like Fillon) but I don't know why. Maybe because she's too cruel? Nah, just kidding

She doesn't like anybody except Trump (and who likes Trump? He's CRAZY)

Chances of being elected president: ENORMOUS APPARENTLY!

I don't have anything against Belgium (I don't even know where it is) but I really really really don't want to live there.

So now I say this prayer every evening →

Dear God, please don't let Marine Le Pen be elected and on my mother's life I'll believe in You. Amen.

(Based on a true story told by Esther A, who is 12 years old)

Riad Sattouf

19

President Esther

I love imagining other lives for myself. So this is what I'd do if I was president of France (LOL)!

1. I'd choose only girls to work with me. Girls are much more intelligent than boys (IMO).

2. I'd crack down on terrorists. They're always attacking people and it's really scary.

3. I'd create special periods where really expensive things went on sale.

4. I'd stop boys insulting and harassing people. All the world's problems are caused by boys in fact.

5. I'd give children more holidays.

6. I'd give raises to people who don't get paid much.

7. Everybody — foreigners, Renois, Rebeus, whoever — would be allowed to come and live in France if they wanted. Except boys, who'd be "chosen on merit" (basically only the nice ones would be allowed in).

8. If Trump tried to call me, I wouldn't answer the phone (because he's horrible and he only works with men anyway). He hates women (apparently he has a mental perversion or something).

9. I'd destroy the Élysée and build a much better building instead (less "chateau", you know?).

10. I'd improve the sewers so we'd have fewer floods.

BUT MOST IMPORTANTLY OF ALL: I'd try to be a "funny" president so people would like me (all humans love to laugh, right?).

(Based on a true story told by Esther A, who is 12 years old)

Riad Sattouf

Zumba

When I was young, I was really into dance. I took classes and stuff and I really liked it (and apparently I was very gifted). I wanted to be a dancer when I grew up.

This is me in "I don't have time for dance now I'm in secondary school" mode

So the other day, I went with my mum to her Zumba class to take my mind off things (you know: school, human cruelty, how boring my life is, etc.).

I was happy to do something with my mum

She's getting fit again (phew!)

We went into this room full of old, overweight women (except for me and the teacher) and it started.

BOOM BOOM BOOM BOOM BOOM BOO

Sorry, I meant "except for me, the teacher and my mum

BOOM ♪ BOOM ♪ BOOM ♪ BOOM ♪ BOOM ♪ BOOM ♪ BOOM ♪ BOOM ♪ BOOM ♪ BOOM ♪ BOOM ♪ BOOM ♪ BOOM ♪ BOOM
ZUMBA EVERYBODY DANCE ZUMBA HOT SOUND POUND IN THE BACKGROUND ZUMBA TO THRILL AND TO CHILL YO ZUMBA GOTTA LOVE THAT HOT SOUND POUNDING YO MAMMA MIA YOU'RE GONNA KIFFE IT ZUMBA YEAH ZUM-BA

x4   x4   x2   x2   x2

It was totally fresh and it all came back to me, like I'd never stopped

While we were dancing I watched my mum and she was doing really well and I was so happy.

ZOUM-BA HEY   ZOUM-BA HA

And suddenly I saw this incredible man

ZOUM-BA HOT SOUND POUNDING

A MOUSE-MAN WITH A MONKEY'S BODY OR SOMETHING

On my mother's life he looked like this

Total mouse head

Effeminate

Hairy like a monkey

He was making these movements and I couldn't tell my mum because we were dancing!

READY TO DANCE YO YOUR BODY HOT AND CLOSE COME TO ME BABE

Afterwards I tried to see him again but there was a crowd of people and he'd disappeared!

MUM! Did you see the guy with the mouse head?

Huh?

DREAM OR REALITY?

WHAT HAPPENED, YO?

(Based on a true story told by Esther A, who is 12 years old)

Riad Sattouf

21

The Future

I often think about the future and stuff. The future is what hasn't happened yet but might happen later. There are films about the future but I think they're all rubbish (dark/scary – not very positive). I don't understand why everybody always imagines that things are going to get worse and worse when there's no way to be sure. Why not imagine the future in "optimistic" mode? That's what I'm going to do (why not?). So it's the year 2100 and I'm 95 years old...

I'd really like to be an editor when I'm older because everybody says I have loads of imagination and I'm good at world-building and stuff... What do you think? Honestly?

(Based on a true story told by Esther A, who is 12 years old)

Riad Sattouf

22

Dictators

I didn't used to care about politics, but I've changed and now I follow what's going on in the world.

This is me and my parents watching a TV debate between all the people who want to be president

My dad told me that if Marine Le Pen wins, we'll move to Belgium (yep, he was serious) so – since I really don't want to do that – I'm trying to work out how to fight against her (I admit I had no idea who she was).

Yeah, she's actually a woman

Afterwards I was a bit surprised (I'd never seen her talk before). I thought she seemed quite nice in fact (sorry if you're offended by that).

She was probably pretending

She smiled sometimes

Because my dad told me she wants to be the dictator of France

You could tell that she would like to be a dictator (that means deciding everything and ordering everyone about).

She saw everything in black and white and never agreed with anybody (in "I know best" mode)

I thought dictators didn't exist any more, but in fact they do. Trump, for example, really really wants to be a dictator.

But apparently he's so crap that he can't manage it, because the Americans won't let him

So he plays golf all the time instead

Then there's Putin in Russia (he likes Trump and Marine Le Pen). Unlike Trump, he's definitely managed to become a dictator.

He gives orders and nobody dares disobey because they don't want to die

I saw a picture of him riding a bear. He's scary because he's not scared of anything.

This is a real photo – just google "Putin and bear"

Look at him!

There's a dictator in Turkey too. His name is El Dog or something (sorry, I don't think that's actually his name).

I don't know anything about him

And I don't really want to (LOL)

He says bad things about us. He hates us but I don't know why.

President Esther, President El Dog has insulted France again, what should we do?

Send him a photo of one of our atomic bombs with this message:

"STOP IT NOW, EL DOG."

I couldn't be a dictator. I wouldn't be capable of forcing people to do stuff.

I've decided to take money from the rich and give it to the needy.

I'm the president of the AOVRP* and we refuse to give money to the poor. It's our money and we want to keep it.

*ASSOCIATION OF VERY RICH PEOPLE

Oh! I understand. But what about this: for one day, you can swap lives with a poor person. So you can experience how it feels to be penniless. And then we'll talk. What do you say?

Hm, I'd never thought of that!

Okay! Let's try it.

FORCE THEM? NO! MAN-IP-YOU-LATE THEM! (LMAO)

(Based on a true story told by Esther A, who is 12 years old)

Riad Sattouf

23

Boys and Girls

You want to know the truth? Okay then, here goes: boys are superior to girls. There, I said it.

For a start, it's boys who decide whether a girl is pretty or ugly.

Boys talk about girls with other boys (judging their looks, style, coolness, etc.) and the "chosen" ones become popular.

Boys also decide who the most popular boys are. Once they've been chosen, they become a sort of leader and the girls start to love them.

It's not unfair, that's just how it is. Boys are stronger, so they're in charge.

Girls who fight against boys are called "feminists". That's okay, but I think they're overreacting a bit because, here in France, girls can still do loads of things.

I think all we need to do to make life better for women in France is to stop boys acting like thugs.

My dad has a gay female cousin. I love her but she's always lecturing me about feminism. If I wear a skirt, she starts saying stuff like it's a problem or something.

Anyway, here in France, life is okay for women. There are other places much worse, like in the Arabias or whatever (where a man can marry, like, ten women at the same time!).

But there are still inequalities between men and women, even in France. For example, there's never been a female president...

But to be honest, I don't mind if a man marries loads of women. It doesn't bother me. Sorry if that offends you, but I'm allowed to think what I want!

But, in return, girls should be able to marry loads of boys too.

(Based on a true story told by Esther A, who is 12 years old)

Riad Sattouf

24

The Very Ancient Race

You remember I have a "special" brother called Antoine?

Pssst, Esther! You know about the reptilians?

Like snakes and stuff? Yeah, I know. I hate them

This is him and me in the bedroom we share

Before, he was a thug and wanted to be a rapper, but this year he's more "normal".

Not reptiles! Reptilians!

They're a mysterious race that control the world apparently

Ha ha well yeah...

Look. YouTube

First I thought it was funny. Then he showed me some YouTube videos and I admit I freaked out (that means "I got really scared" in the language of the street), even if you can tell it's sort of fake.

?

Here's the proof...

The reptilians are supposedly an intelligent species of beings descended from dinosaurs who live underground. They secretly control humans for mysterious reasons.

Us humans come from monkeys

The reptilians come from dinosaurs

They're not extraterrestrials because they're from Earth! I think that's the scary part. Apparently some of them take human form and are famous celebrities exercising power over society.

The Queen of England is an extremely old and powerful reptilian

She NEVER blinks

Intriguing, right?

One of the ways you can recognize them

To spot a reptilian, you have to watch their eyes in the videos. From time to time, their REAL and SERIOUSLY FREAKY eyes become visible for a fraction of a second.

All American presidents are reptilians

That would explain a LOT...

Pointy ears: another sign!

To start with, people believed Obama wasn't one, but in fact he is

Incredible but true: Francois Hollande is also a reptilian. He looks so nice... but I saw a video where you can see his real eyes.

You see him looking at a toy submarine (weird)

Gasp!

Reptilian eyes

My brother explained that they all know one another and they pretend to be humans to take revenge on us and lead us to our downfall.

The reptilians are a very ancient race who are dying out... They hate humans because they're jealous of us...

Even if it's not true, I adore this kind of stuff: the mysterious secrets of the world, etc. I'd like to read books about that (which is why I dream of being an editor).

Reptilians? Excellent. Lots of potential...

Soon there'll be an election to choose the next French president. Which of them do you think could be reptilians?*

(Based on a true story told by Esther A, who is 12 years old)

Riad Sattouf

*Just kidding – I think they're all human.

25

Politics

Everything has gone well at my new school. I haven't had any problems adapting or mixing with kids from a different social background.

The people in my class aren't interested in politics at all (except for making fun of Trump).

The students know there's an election coming but, well, life goes on.

They mostly talk about how good-looking or ugly the candidates are, because it's important: if they get elected, you'll see them everywhere (so it's better if they're good-looking).

I tell you: it's Marine Le Pen. She's fresh.

I was shocked by this because I don't like Marine Le Pen (you know why, right? If she's elected, we'll have to move to a distant land called Belgium and I don't want to do that!).

Eva explained that Marine Le Pen would be extremely harsh on the Islamists or whatever and hunt them down in "ruthless" mode, so she liked her.

Then she showed me a website that calculated each candidate's chances of being elected and Le Pen had, like, a really big score.

I don't know who Macron is either, or what he wants to do... but since he seems to be the only one who can defeat Marine Le Pen, I like him.

And then Eva told me that her parents were Le Pen supporters and they were going to vote for her!

(Based on a true story told by Esther A, who is 12 years old)

Riad Sattouf

26

The Pancake

As I get older, I seem to be developing a passion for the world of cuisine.

This is me on holiday at my granny's house watching "Top Chef", a brilliant TV show about cooking

My parents were in Saint-Malo, the town with dogs on the beach

I like the candidates' energy and creativity and the fact that they're all competing against each other and one of them will be the winner.

We're going to make a carrot reduction, which we'll mix with caramel, varying the textures so that there's a combination of crunchiness and smoothness and a satisfying harmony in the mouth

I also love their "pro" way of talking

I'd thought that I wanted to be an editor when I grew up, but now I have this new passion I'm not sure any more...

Granny, can I try to make a meal out of what's in the fridge?

Of course

A half-eaten saucisson, some leftover shop-bought raclette, some mini-Babybel cheese, apricot jam...

All we need is... Hey! PER-FECT.

A pancake almost past its sell-by date

And now I'm just going to give free rein to my creativity!

I rubbed butter on the pancake to liven it up a bit (it was dry and brittle)

Having fun

Then, in one half of the pancake, I sprinkled bits of the raclette and the Babybel cheese

On top I placed a few slices of saucisson for its colour and the play of chaud-froid

Mmm, the smell of hot cheese

In the other half: big spoonfuls of jam

Smells of apricot and springtime

My idea was to have the main course and the dessert on the same pancake (clever, right?)

That looks good, my dear, but sweet-and-savoury is not really my thing

Me in "proud" mode

That suited me! I ate it all and it was delicious (saucisson and apricot is a surprisingly great combination IMO – you should try it!)

The salty, generous flavour of melted cheese

And the playful sweetness of the jam

Then suddenly I asked:

Who are you going to vote for, Granny?

Well, I was going to vote for Le Pen, but given that your dad says he'll move to Belgium if she wins, I don't know now.

WTF

(Based on a true story told by Esther A, who is 12 years old)

Riad Sattouf

27

The Illuminati

When I discovered that my grandmother had been planning to vote for Marine Le Pen, I was, like, totally shocked.

"This is her and me in "are you serious?" mode."

I was annoyed

There are too many foreigners in France and nobody does anything.

My grandmother lives in Bain-de-Bretagne, in Brittany. She told me that when she came to Paris to see us, some Rebeus spat at her for no reason and ever since then she's been afraid of them and wanted them to go away.

Granny! It's not a Rebeu thing to spit on girls, it's a boy thing!

All boys spit on girls!

That's life!

Thankfully, my dad played his "Belgium" card and my grandmother changed her mind (it's good to be able to change your mind).

I'll vote for Melenchon then, like your father...

Afterwards, my parents and my brothers came back from their walk and everybody talked politics. We discussed who would face Marine Le Pen in the final vote (because she'll be there no matter what, apparently).

Melenchon will get through to the second round for sure...

HAHA no way...

Melenchon wants to take money from the rich and give it to the poor (which is, honestly, the right thing to do, so it's not surprising that my dad likes him – my dad is a good man).

Oh, and you think Hamon will make it?

He'll surprise everyone!

Hamon is a very nice candidate who wants to give money to everybody (not just the poor). I must admit I like him.

I'm sick of the left. I'm just saying it like I see it.

Thanks for that, Mum.

If I were you, I'd vote Macron because he's an Illuminati, yo

And the Illuminati always win

Antoine explained that Macron had worked for "Roz Child" or something, this secret bank that controls the world, and that this was the bank of the Illuminati, a mysterious sect whose symbol is a freaky pyramid with an eye on top – which is also on the dollar!

It's a really scary, mysterious drawing, right? →

← It really is on dollar bills – shady, don't you think?

Italian writing →

That eye gives me the shivers

My dad laughed at him and said he'd rather Antoine believed in the Illuminati than took drugs.

But in fact Melenchon and Hamon lost, and it was Macron and Le Pen in the final round, just like my brother said!

On the night of the vote, he didn't look surprised

I wish I was an Illuminati...

... you control the world and stuff...

And... Emmanuel Macron comes out in front...

I was impressed

(Based on a true story told by Esther A, who is 12 years old)

Riad Sattouf

Ed Sheeran

So I saw part of the debate between Macron and Le Pen on TV.

This is me and my family thinking 'That Le Pen woman is off her head'

I mean, when she made those hand movements and said that her voters were hidden here and there, was she serious? I felt sooo sorry for her.

THEY'RE HEEERE IN THE COUNTRYSIIIIDE EVERYWHEEEERE

My evil witch impression

So while we wait for the election to take place, I'm going to talk about a feel-good song that everyone's listening to. That way, if Le Pen is the new president by the time you read this, it'll help you relax a bit.

The song is called "Shape of You"

I think it's about a girl's body.

And the singer is called Aide Shiranne (although he spells it Ed Sheeran)

Ed Sheeran is a ginger

Funny, simple face

Passionate about his art

Tattoos all over his body

Massively famous

I don't usually like gingers, I must admit, because looking at their reddish-orange hair gets repetitive after a while.

I don't feel the same way about other hair colours

I'm so glad I'm not a ginger

Unfair, I know

Sorry gingers (LOL)

The video for the song is really good IMO. It starts with Ed Sheeran going to the gym.

A lone wolf

Crazy about boxing

And then he sees this ultra-beautiful Chinese-Renoi who's training for some kind of combat sport, in "independent" mode

She does this and Ed Sheeran is impressed by her bendiness

Yep, I can do it too

Afterwards she hits a punchbag

Then she accidentally hurts him by opening the door of his changing room (clumsy) and that's how they meet (romantic).

Warning: cuteness overdose (LOL)

So they go to a restaurant and he orders this enormous plate of chicken or something and he's in "I'm starving after all that sport" mode. It's really funny.

They become friends and then they fall in love, united by their shared passion for sport

Then there's this totally crazy part where Ed Sheeran puts on this "fat-man" costume and he has to fight this obese Chinese guy who's called a Zulu wrestler or something.

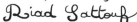

He gets destroyed — so funny

This is him!

And at the end, the Chinese-Renoi girl attacks the Zulu to save her beloved Ed. Moral: love is a combat sport and you have to both be warriors to survive.

Warrior girl saving her lover

All Ed Sheeran's videos get, like, a billion views on YouTube (he's the most famous man on the planet). But when I mentioned him to my dad:

I am in love with the shape of you la la

Aide Shiranne? Never heard of him. Is he well known?

Crazy, right? My poor sweet daddy is totally disconnected from reality!

(Based on a true story told by Esther A, who is 12 years old)

Riad Sattouf

The Illuminettes

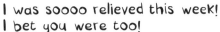

I was soooo relieved this week! I bet you were too!

This is me when I found out we wouldn't have to move to Belgium (as my dad threatened to do if Le Pen won)

YEEEEAAAAH

And Emmanuel Macron is the new president of

Then Macron gave a speech in front of a pyramid in the Louvre in "I'm the boss" mode.

My brother

Macron

Whoa, shady!

Together for France

Don't you get it, yo? Macron in front of the pyramid?

The eye at the top of the pyramid!

? ?

GAAASP! THAT THING YOU WERE TALKING ABOUT! THE ILLUMINETTES!

And then my whole family burst out laughing (because I said "Illuminettes" instead of "Illuminati").

HA HA HA HA HA HA

My brother was annoyed because nobody was listening to him now

Whaaaat? Ha ha

The Illuminati are these people who secretly control the world and their symbol is a pyramid with an eye on top. Antoine had told us all that Macron was one of them.

After his speech in front of the pyramid, everyone started saying "Hey, Macron's an Illuminati"...

My brother the visionary

Nobody ever listens to me, it pisses me off

After that, I had an idea for a series of YA mystery/comedy novels called "The Illuminettes" (which could also be made into a TV series).

At a prestigious secondary school in Paris, Milena, the most popular student, disappears.

So then a very pretty girl called Carla (I really like that name) becomes the new most popular girl in the school.

Carla, will you come to my birthday party?

Carla!

Carla! I love you

A modest girl, she's not at ease with her new position, but she has to deal with it

Aren't her clothes beautiful?

That evening, she receives a letter marked with a black pyramid, announcing that – as the most popular girl in her school – she is now an Illuminette, a girl who has many powers over other people.

SECRET

Congratulations, you are now an Illuminette but your life is in grave danger...

She discovers that there's an Illuminette in each school, controlling her "people" of submissive girls, and that there's a ruthless war between the Illuminettes...

Pretty girl

Pulling strings

For their own good

Girls doing what they can

... and the Illuminos, the popular boys, who also have a secret organization and want to control the world!

Carla has to investigate them, taking terrible risks...

Careful you don't go too far, Carla...

?!

What do you think? I'd like to be a chef or an editor when I'm older. I like using the mysteries of life to imagine the beginnings of stories...

If anyone wants to write the rest, my idea is for sale: one billion euros please

Joke

(Based on a true story told by Esther A, who is 12 years old)

Riad Sattouf

Rebellion

I haven't got into too much trouble in my life. Even if I'm often tempted to break the rules, I usually don't dare. To be honest I'm often too scared.

This is me on the bus — I haven't swiped my ticket, but I'm staying close to the machine in case a ticket inspector comes along, so I can swipe it at the last minute

When I was in Year 1, I'd ask the teacher if I could go to the toilet, she'd say yes, and I'd go downstairs and just walk straight past the girls' bathroom. I was really scared.

But I couldn't help myself!

I would challenge myself to go a bit further each time: the end of the corridor, the headmaster's door, all the way to the street!

HEY YOU!

I was relieved that he stopped me before the worst could happen

One day in Year 4, I was late to school and the others were already in class. But instead of going into the classroom, I walked through the corridors and explored the school.

Again, I couldn't help myself

In "crazy" mode

And again, I was stopped before I could open a mysterious wooden door at the end of a corridor.

What was behind it? Another world? (LOL)

Let me see... what else? I cut up an umbrella with scissors once because I was bored.

At home, in "I don't give a shit" mode

In Year 5 I had loads of lovers so I wrote romantic messages on the wall of my bedroom.

My mum really shouted at me afterwards

E+M = ♡
E+L = ♡
E+T = ♡♡
E+N = ♡

Oh, and then there was the shoplifting. One day, I tried on a scarf in a shop and then walked out still wearing it. But the alarm went off!

Wiiiii Wiii Wiii

"Oh, sorry!"

"I forgot to take it off"

I'm a good actress when I'm scared

I also had a friend called Eugenie who was SOOOO rich. I often stole nail varnish from her (she had loads of different colours that she never used).

OOOH this video of TAL is soo good

Oh yeah?

But I must admit that the worst thing I ever did wasn't very long ago. I spat at some old lady from my window.

The temptation was too strong

I didn't really think it would hit her

Afterwards I had a panic attack: what if someone had filmed me? And if I was arrested or something? Why did I do that to some poor old lady? She could have been my grandmother!

Esther, how could you?

Sorry Dad

I wanted to apologize to her but it was too late, so I cried all night instead.

Rebellion really isn't my thing

(Based on a true story told by Esther A, who is 12 years old)

Riad Sattouf

The Terrorist Attack

At my secondary school, there's a different teacher for each subject (not like primary school, where there's just one teacher). I think it's better this way. I like seeing different faces.

The other day, something traumatic happened. Honestly, it was terrible.

"Diversity, relatedness and unity of living beings. Answer true or false:
1. A male green frog can reproduce with a female red frog..."

Hmm, that should work...

So anyway, we were in the middle of a test and suddenly this really weird alarm went off.

WEEEEEEEEEEE

And the teacher just started acting... well, weird.

WEEEEEEEEEEE

I... um... Wait... What's... Um...

And then Cassiopee (the best student in the class) said:

That's not the fire alarm, it's a military alarm! It means the school's being attacked!

Then the teacher freaked out and started screaming.

EVERYBODY UNDER THE TABLES! EVERYBODY UNDER THE TABLES! TERRORIST ATTACK!

And then it was just total panic. We all cowered under the tables. The alarm kept wailing...

WEEE

I didn't understand what was going on. I was thinking "There's not really a terrorist attack, is there? This isn't actually happening..."

Eva, a good friend of mine, lost it completely (I was, like, in a dream or something)...

EEEE

It's happening, girl, it's happening

Some boys (the feminists) were crying. A "feminist boy" is one who admits being weak, not tough, and who hangs around with girls.

WEEEEE

I'm too young to die I'm too young to die

On my father's life, he really said that

Of course the insensitive boys just laughed, in "who gives a shit" mode.

WEEE

WEEEEE

Some of them played with their fidget spinners and said stuff like

Who gives a flying fuck? It's just a stupid exercise

After a while, I heard the sound of students in the courtyard, so I said:

Miss! I think we have to go outside! Everybody else is out there!

Our saviour (LOL)

I... Yes! OUTSIDE! EVERYBODY OUT!

(Based on a true story told by Esther A, who is 12 years old)

Riad Sattouf

The Alarm

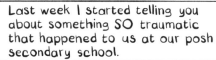

Last week I started telling you about something SO traumatic that happened to us at our posh secondary school.

WEEE   WEEEEE

This is me and my classmates evacuating the building because of the alarm!

We all found ourselves in the courtyard and it was totally packed with the entire school in there.

WEEEEE   WEEEE

Everybody was talking and stuff

It was like a concert or something

Then the headmaster spoke into a megaphone (this thing that makes your voice louder) and he said:

Silence! You're making far too much noise! The terrorists can hear you! YOU'RE ALL DEAD NOW!

Afterwards, he asked for four minutes' silence and the students shut up a bit. Then Eva pointed out a loudspeaker in the courtyard.

Imagine if a voice came out of that and said "Dear students, the terrorists are coming to kill you. Don't move."

AND THEN SUDDENLY, ON MY MOTHER'S LIFE...

DEAR STUDENTS...

GASP!

... please walk calmly back to your classrooms. The evacuation exercise is over.

We went back to the classroom and then the teacher did this weird performance where she acted like we'd all forgotten that she'd totally lost it, thinking that there really WAS a terrorist attack instead of understanding that it was just an exercise.

Well, I have something to tell you all. I'm sorry, but...

... if there really was a terrorist attack, it would make no difference how you reacted. You would all die anyway.

SERIOUSLY, THAT'S WHAT SHE SAID!

Us in "um, WHAT did she say?" mode

If there's an attack and you find yourself face to face with a terrorist, I would advise you to do nothing. Don't move.

Everyone who's ever tried to run away or talk them out of it... they've all died.

With no exceptions.

So perhaps if you do nothing and just look at them without moving, they won't do anything?

Help me, I'm in shock... is she really saying this to children?

It's worth a try

(Based on a true story told by Esther A, who is 12 years old)

Riad Sattouf

33

Flying

The other day, everyone in my family was asleep and I snuck out into the street, in "I'm free" mode.

This is me thinking how weird it is that there's nobody else around

Then I discovered that if I jumped in the air and made a breaststroke movement...

I would hover above the ground

I started swimming through the air and flew up over the rooftops!

Strange they never told us we could do this at school!

Suddenly I saw a sort of gigantic church in the distance.

Weird... I never knew that existed!

A light at the top!

A restaurant! I think I'll stop there for a rest!

Restaurant

Good evening, miss. Please take a seat. We were expecting you.

Thank you, my good man.

I sat down in "there's a restaurant at the top of a huge church AND they were expecting me?!?" mode.

Only flyers can eat here, you see...

Ah. I see.

And then he brought me this enormous strawberry Tagada (just my favourite sweet in the whole world!)

I took a bite and it wasn't sweet at all — it was warm and slightly salty

But I ate it anyway LOL

It was a dream, of course, not reality. (I REALLY wish I could find out if any readers believed me when they read the first few panels! That would be sooo funny!)

The next morning, I tried to do the flying breaststroke

I'm crazy

Well, you never know! It could have been us humans' secret gift and nobody had ever tried!

(Based on a true story told by Esther A, who is 12 years old)

Riad Sattouf

34

The Wound

Something tragic happened this week that really made me grow up. I learned two important things: 1. Just because you love something doesn't mean it loves you back, and 2. You should never underestimate the call of the wild. As you know, I have a Russian hamster called Manuela, and I really loved her (like a big sister or something). So, the other day, I wanted to take her out of her cage and give her a hug. I really thought she'd be pleased — that it would make her happy. So anyway, I opened the cage to pick her up...

(Based on a true story told by Esther A, who is 12 years old)

Riad Sattouf

Happiness

We don't spend enough time talking about happiness! I want to talk about a place where I feel very happy: the cafeteria.

This is me and my girls lining up for food

After a boring morning of classes, I adore meeting up with my friends to laugh and talk about different stuff in "relaxed" mode.

We're in Year 7 *Eva* *Capucine* *Lea*

It clears my head, being with them and seeing them happy to be with me.

It warms my heart too *Beautiful, right? (LOL)*

Sometimes we act crazy to deal with the stress of life...

... and we just laugh hysterically.

When I get too happy, I look at the disabled table and think how that could have been me, and it brings me back down to earth.

Nobody laughing here

In my school, the disabled kids go to regular classes to make them feel like they have normal lives and stuff.

But I have to be honest: nobody speaks to them because, you know, they're disabled

At mealtime, though, their helpers or whatever they're called bring them all to the same table.

These are the adults who look after them

What's sad is that there's one of them who looks normal but who eats with them anyway. It's because he's just "a bit" disabled.

He actually has some normal friends, but...

... HE HAS TO EAT WITH HIS PEOPLE. THAT'S JUST HOW IT IS.

I don't know what his disability is *His mouth just sticks out like this*

Sometimes, I imagine that a helper will come and get me and take me to the loonies' table even though I thought I was normal.

Come on, you need to be with others like you.

I...

Total nightmare

Comparing my life to the lives of others is a good way to make me feel happy.

I'm so lucky to be normal and have friends who love me

(Based on a true story told by Esther A, who is 12 years old)

Riad Sattouf

Money

When I was little, I used to love money.

This is me in "but today I don't give a shit" mode

HAHA! MONEY!

WHO NEEDS IT?

This cartoon panel is a joke — in real life I don't throw money away

Money is something that's used to buy stuff. But unlike food or drink, money is not necessary to life.

For example, you can live in the wild without money

Berries to eat

River water to drink

But since human beings are lazy, they use money to make life simple.

Bottle of Cristaline bought with money

GLUG GLUG GLUG

Strawberries from the supermarket

The first time I had money, it was the tooth fairy who gave it to me.

I got 1 euro in exchange for my tooth!

The first thing I bought with money was a farty rubber pig.

PFRRRT

It made this noise when you pressed on it (hilarious)

I never asked my parents for money. I didn't want to be a burden on them... But one day, my dad said:

Esther, sweetheart! I'd like to give you some pocket money every month. So you can learn to manage cash.

Huh? Naah, there's no need

But my dad insisted, so to make him happy I accepted.

We agreed on the sum of 5 euros

Every month I get a piece of paper with a number 5 on it (LOL)

Since I don't know what else to do with it, I buy gifts for my parents to thank them for looking after me since my birth.

I gave my beloved father a necklace with a "wolf" charm that symbolizes "family"

For my mum, the same but with a hummingbird to symbolize "happiness"

I didn't give anything to my little brother (too young) or to my brother Antoine.

Besides, I couldn't find an animal to symbolize stupidity...

(Just kidding! He's actually less stupid now that he's interested in conspiracy theories)

For the first time, a video shows the reality of the Bohemian Club, the most evil secret society of all time

Whoa... fuuuck

The two necklaces cost me 15 euros (yep, you read that right: three months of pocket money)!

What can I say? I adore my parents!

At school, though, I'm pretty much the exception.

5 euros? Are you kidding, girl? How do you manage?

My friend Eva

I get 500 euros a month and I can hardly make ends meet...

Yes, that's right, we're in Year 7

(Based on a true story told by Esther A, who is 12 years old)

Riad Sattouf

Wealth

This year, I'm in Year 7 at a public (that means free) secondary school in the centre of Paris (which means there are loads of rich kids, because you have to be wealthy to live there).

This is me, shocked to discover that Eva gets 500 euros a month in pocket money

GASP! Will you show me?

I get 5 euros

Every month she gets the equivalent of 8 years of pocket money for me.

I'd be 20 before I got that much!

I can't girl, it's in the bank

What can she possibly do with all that money? I wouldn't have a clue how to spend it.

With 500 euros, you could buy 1,000 "Head Bangers"

They're sour sweets

That's more than a lifetime supply!

Some months I go crazy and spend it all on clothes and gadgets...

And I'm broke by the 20th...

Other times I do my little banker act — I spend nothing and at the end of 3 months I have 1,500 euros, yo.

So funny!

I'd never tell her this but I'm shocked that children get paid so much. When I think about all the poor people in the world eating nothing but twigs...

... I could almost weep

When I'm a grown-up, though, I'd like to be very rich and have at least 20,000 euros (with that much, you probably wouldn't have to worry about anything).

10 a.m.... No need to get up — I've got 20,000 euros in my bank account...

Maitre Gims and Black M are VERY rich, of course. Fame and fortune go hand in hand.

I bet they've got at least a million each

The singer Adele is one of the richest women in the world. Apparently she's got billions (although I don't listen to her music).

She's succeeded despite huge weight problems (obesity), poor thing

She deserves it

My parents aren't rich. I would guess they've got about 2,000 euros?

My dad really hates the rich — it's hilarious

DO YOU REALLY NEED YOUR BIG FAT TURBO SUV IN PARIS, YOU PRICK?!

Oh stop being an old man, yo... You'd love it if you were rich...

NOT AT ALL

Antoine my crazy brother

You're JEALOUS of the rich, just like all POOR PEOPLE

WHAT?!

Watch the road

(Based on a true story told by Esther A, who is 12 years old)

Riad Sattouf

38

The Power of Analytical Thinking

Last week my brother Antoine accused my dad of "dreaming of being rich, like all poor people" (yep, he went there).

This is me watching my dad fume because he hates the rich

My mum laughing

HaHa

I'd rather not answer that...

For a while now, Antoine has loved having debates with my dad (he always thinks the exact opposite of him).

If you had millions, you wouldn't want the poor to take it from you. You'd be just like all rich people...

HA HA!

Nah, but you're not being logical, you know... You moan about the rich and that, but you did everything you could to make sure Esther went to a posh school...

For the quality of the teaching, not the social class

Pfft

Okay, and if "the quality of the teaching" helps Esther succeed and become mega-rich, what will you do? Hate her?

Naaah...

My brother gets on my nerves but he's not always wrong. It's true that my dad would like to be rich (but he doesn't want to admit it).

... because you don't just hope that she'll become rich...

He knows that he'll never get rich working in a gym, so hating the rich is a way of venting his frustration.

... you hope that she'll GIVE YOU MONEY! That's why you want her to be educated!

I feel sorry for my poor dad. It hurts him.

Antoine, I preferred it when you banged on about Nekfeu or the Illuminati

Sarcasm... Because you've been outwitted by my powers of analytical thinking, yo! Ha ha out-WIT-ted!

HEY, STOP HAVING A GO AT HIM!

Yes, I want to be, like, MEGA-RICH and yes, I'll GIVE ALL MY MONEY TO DAD!

So what? What're you gonna do about it?

Nothing!

The powers of analytical thiiiiinkiiiing!

He's right!

(Based on a true story told by Esther A, who is 12 years old)

Riad Sattouf

39

The Horror Story

The other night I had a sleepover at Cassandra's house. She was my best friend in primary school and now she's at a private secondary school and her dad died when we were in Year 5 and... You remember who she is, right? Anyway...

This is me and her in the same bed in "trying to freak each other out with horror stories" mode

Listen to this. It's a true story...

One day, when she was a child, my aunt went to an antique dealer with her father. And there, in a window display, she saw...

Daddy, look! What a pretty doll! I want it!

The old saleswoman, who looked like a skeleton, said: "That's the tic-tac doll, young lady, and she's not for sale."

Couldn't we come to an agreement? Here's 1,000 euros

The rich father managed to convince the old lady. But as they were leaving...

Watch out! At night, you must lock the tic-tac doll in a cupboard! If you don't... SOMETHING TERRIBLE WILL HAPPEN!

Yeah okay, bye!

Back at home, my aunt played with the doll then put it in a cupboard in the basement.

No need to lock it...

She went to bed and fell asleep. But suddenly, in the middle of the night, she heard:

TIC-TAC TIC-TAC I'M IN THE CUPBOARD

TIC-TAC TIC-TAC I'M OUT OF THE CUPBOARD

TIC-TAC TIC-TAC I'M IN THE HALLWAY

TIC-TAC TIC-TAC I'M OUTSIDE YOUR DOOR

TIC-TAC-TIC-TAC I'M GOING TO KILL YOU

TIC-TAC-TIC BOOO!

Honestly I was terrified, I think my heart actually stopped beating for a few seconds.

Very funny!

It's weird how I like being scared

(Based on a true story told by Esther A, who is 12 years old)

Riad Sattouf

40

Areas with Major Constraints

This year, one of the things I learned that's stayed with me was about "areas with major constraints".

In fact they're places where people live that have lots of constraints, making life there more difficult than where we live.

For a start, there are HOT DESERTS. Terribly high temperatures, no water or hospitals, few towns, living in tents...

Of course the well is soooooooo far away (20 km in fact) and I'm the only one who can go there. And then I have to come back.

Next, there are COLD DESERTS (North and South Pole, Siberia, tundra...)

And then there are all the animals constantly attacking us because they're cold and hungry too...

After that, there are HIGH MOUNTAINS, where it's impossible to build roads or have electricity and the air's too thin to breathe...

And SMALL ISLANDS: people think they're paradise because the weather's good but there's nothing to do so you're totally bored...

It made me realize how lucky I was to be born, by pure chance, in Paris. Thank you, chance!

At the same time, I share my bedroom with my brother Antoine who listens to PNL at top volume on his headphones (PNL is a rap group formed by drug dealers but I don't understand any of the words).

In fact MY BEDROOM is an area of major constraints (LOL)

(Based on a true story told by Esther A, who is 12 years old)

Riad Sattouf

41

Writing

I started writing a novel this week (reading is one of my passions). I'm just trying to see if I can do it (I want to be an editor when I grow up).

I like stories where the narrator says "I", you know, where it's like someone telling their story in "diary" mode... I don't like it so much when "she" does this or that.

I also like mystery, horror, action, monsters and anything romantic.

The title of my book is: "Memoirs of a Teenage Vampire".

Mysterious, right?

In fact, I imagined what would happen if I became a vampire. In a totally realistic way. It all starts one night when I'm alone at home...

Suddenly I hear <u>a child crying</u> outside...

And then... OMG! A little girl is hanging on the window ledge. If she falls, she could die!

Help me, I beg you! Let me inside!

I'm going to fall

Because I'm gentle and compassionate, I help her and invite her into my bedroom... BIG MISTAKE!

It'll be okay, little girl! What are your parents called?

Waah

Her eyes are so blue and so deep... I look into them and I'm spellbound...

You were nice to me so I won't kill you now... In fact, I'm going to give you a beautiful gift...

The next morning I wake up with the vague memory of a strange, scary dream...

In the kitchen my parents are eating breakfast...

Morning, Esther!

Oh sweetie, you've got acne... There are two spots on your neck...

I run to the bathroom.

(Based on a true story told by Esther A, who is 12 years old)

Riad Sattouf

42

The Icy Wind

I think I like writing my book. Even if it's pretty exhausting.

This is me rereading the first 10 pages

Serious stuff

In last week's episode: after helping a little vampire girl, I was bitten by her. What will happen now?

This scarf should be perfect for hiding the teeth marks...

I can still see myself in the mirror... ...so everything's okay

I go to school as normal. I feel kind of floaty...

The light hurts my eyes a little, but it's not a problem...

... I have my heart-shaped sunglasses

Yeah, it's raining. So what?

I don't take them off in the classroom. The teacher says something about this. "The light hurts me, I'm keeping them on," I say in an echoey voice that frightens the old lady.

Oh... Ok-k-kay Esther, as you like...

At lunch in the cafeteria, the food makes me feel sick... but no more than normal...

Um... Are you sure you're okay, girl? You look kinda weird

Yeah... I just hate these vegetables

I love the colour of your sweater though.

At the end of the day, some bad boys from Year 10 insult me for no reason as usual.

Hey, give us those sunglasses, ho

Before I even realize what's happening, his throat is pulsating in my hands. He suffocates like a fish out of water.

You've... already... got... glasses... dickhead

Ach

Disturbing little voice

Scared by my own strength, I vanish like a shadow while the ambulance sirens scream...

A pleasantly icy wind sweeps me away

At home, I feel refreshed by the dusk, and as soon as the sun goes down I'm filled with energy.

Hello sweetie...

My dad coming home from work

What a beautiful daughter I have! You just get prettier every day...

MWAH

(Based on a true story told by Esther A, who is 12 years old)

Riad Sattouf

The Murder

I'm making good progress on my book about vampires!

This is me in "counting the pages again" mode

I've already written 12 pages!

Not bad, right?

In last week's episode: one day after being bitten, I notice the first changes in my body and I'm shocked.

After almost biting my father, I ran to my bedroom before I could do something unforgivable

I tell him I'm feeling ill so I can stay under the covers.

Do you want something to eat? Shall I call a doctor?

NO, DON'T CALL! I'm... I'm fine, I just need to rest!

Now get out and LEAVE ME ALONE!

When everybody is asleep, I'm lured into the night.

I'm starving, so I jump out the window in "this seems normal" mode

Ow, I bit my lip when I hit the ground

GASP!

At that moment, I see the building's concierge staring at me from the hallway.

Weird but true: that ugly woman looks as delicious to me as a four cheese pizza!

I kill her because I'm still a beginner vampire (yeah, I like horror when it's funny) and the blood gets everywhere.

I come back to myself and start worrying about the consequences of my act, which has covered the hall in blood.

GASP but... but... what will my parents think when they find out that I...

Who cares? Why does it matter if they find out? You're not one of them any more...

THE LITTLE VAMPIRE GIRL WHO CREATED ME!

Look what a mess you made! I'm going to have to teach you...

...MY DAUGHTER.

(Based on a true story told by Esther A, who is 12 years old)

Riad Sattouf

44

The Difficulty of Writing

Writing is really hard. It requires imagination and motivation. I know because I started writing a book...

This is me looking at my iPhone 3 instead of writing my story

It was bound to happen (LOL)

Us youngsters are lazy

... and it's really really difficult to stay concentrated and control everything.

With each blank page, you have to start again at zero

It's looong

Plus, writing a horror story like this gets you thinking about weird stuff that you wouldn't normally think about...

It can be a bit depressing

For example, if you're a vampire, that means you're dead, cursed and... <u>eternal</u>.

You stay young and pretty for ever (which is good)...

But being eternal also means watching all your "non-vampire" loved ones die.

Seeing my dad die of old age... how horrifying

Beep-beep

Beep-beep

Not only that, but you're watching your loved ones die while desperately wanting to suck all their blood!

It really disgusts me, thinking about that

Beep-beep

Beep-beep

Then I thought of a less tragic solution: I could turn my whole family into vampires to keep them close to me.

Even my little brother who would be, like, the youngest vampire ever.

Mummy!

This is funny but also sad: imagine being 2 for ever!

And then imagining my brother Antoine as a vampire annoying me for eternity... that was annoying

Esther SUCKS! Ha ha ha geddit?

I even imagined that I'd visit President Macron and turn him into a vampire (crazy idea, right?)

Come here, my pretty!

Yes he sleeps with a flag – he's the president

There are so many possibilities when you're writing, and you have to make all these choices...

MWAH!

... I think I'll stick to being a reader and an editor.

(Based on a true story told by Esther A, who is 12 years old)

Riad Sattouf

45

Shame

Year 7 is over, so Eva and I organized a party to celebrate!

This is me and my dad, who's congratulating me on my school report (yep, I did well)

← Look how happy he is!

We invited almost the whole class to Luxembourg (it's a public garden near our school) for a "party"-style picnic.

We went shopping (juice, sweets, etc.)

Get some Innocent

Oh yeah!

We sat on the grass in the sun. It was sooo nice.

And suddenly one of the boys started throwing water at another boy...

... and it turned into this massive water fight!!!

After a while, three boys poured WHOLE BOTTLES of water on me!

How we laughed →

When suddenly...

?

HEY... ?

We'd moved away from our bags and some guy was rummaging through them!

THAT'S OURS! THAT'S OURS!

And then he started yelling at us that he hated us and that rich kids like us were the worst people in the world or something...

Plus loads of swear words that grown-ups don't normally say to children

So anyway we shouted at him and in the end he went away. Nobody came to help us!

Fuck you! Fuck you all!

We just wanted him to stop going through our stuff – what's wrong with him?

That was when I noticed that everyone in the park was looking at ME

The water had made my dress transparent ↙

(Based on a true story told by Esther A, who is 12 years old)

Riad Sattouf

46

The African Dream

The other night I dreamed of Africa (this really beautiful place that I hope to visit one day).

This is me walking through the savannah in "no worries" mode

I'm not afraid of lions or tigers. I know nothing can happen to me here because the animals of the savannah respect me.

Suddenly in the distance I see an unfamiliar shape...

HA HA HA
IT'S GOT A MAN'S EARS!

HA HA! I DON'T BELIEVE IT!

I'm laughing hysterically. I want to tell the elephant I'm sorry, that I can't help it, but it's impossible because I'm laughing too hard... So it gets REALLY ANNOYED and storms off.

HANG ON, I...
BAHAHAHAHAA

And I woke up laughing!

HAHA

FUNNY, RIGHT?

(Based on a true story told by Esther A, who is 12 years old)

Riad Sattouf

The Romani

Do you know about the Romani?

This is me with my dad in the street, looking at them

They're poor tramps with no country who beg and sleep on the streets of our cities.

I could easily be her (sad face)

Why doesn't anybody help them (government, president or whatever)? Can someone answer me?

The other day, Cassandra and me went out in "old friends reunited" mode

She's doing fine actually

We walked past a group of Romani sitting on the ground and a boy looked at us. He was _very_ good-looking.

Dark eyes

He even had stylish clothes

I smiled at him!

AND THEN... WELL, HE STARTED FOLLOWING US!

Umm, we have a problem, Esther

I turned around and he smiled at me.

He had a sparkling smile, literally: one of his teeth was gold!

Cassandra totally freaked. Apparently she's scared of Romani people so she shouted "Run!"

He's going to kidnap us!

And when we turned around again...

He was still there! On my mother's life, he'd run after us.

I'M SCARED!

So we went into a bakery...

Then he disappeared

What did he want? Why did he scare us after I'd smiled at him? Did he think I was making fun of him? Or what if we were wrong about all of it?

I regretted running, I admit

What if he felt rejected? Poor Romani people! The French government should give them their own département, so that could be their country.

Like the Auvergne, maybe?

Apparently nobody lives there

They could call it Romie? Or Romania (but wait, that already exists). Or even Romance! Or another name...

I think that would be nice for them

(Based on a true story told by Esther A, who is 12 years old)

Riad Sattouf

48

Kisses

Do you like kisses? I do.

This is me kissing my wrist so I can feel what other people feel when I kiss them

Have you noticed that it's possible to analyse someone's personality by the way they kiss?

A kiss is when your mouth turns into a little suction pad and makes a sort of wet sound

MMWAH!

Everybody on this planet should kiss each other instead of fighting, don't you think? (I make myself laugh like crazy when I say that kind of thing).

Apparently you have to kiss at least four people a day to be happy

Myth or reality?

For example, my dad's kisses (which I adore).

A series of very quick kisses

Mwah mwah mwah mwah

It's a technique to get in lots of kisses in the time normally reserved for just one kiss.

Mwah mwah mwah mwah

Clever

Personality: enjoys life 150%

I like my mum's kisses too. They're like little mouth tickles. They make me laugh.

She attacks by surprise

Personality: mischievous (yep, that's her)

I'm trying to train my little brother to kiss. Impossible. He won't even try and that GETS ON MY NERVES!

DO IT — ON MY CHEEK!

WAAAH

Personality: rebellious and impossible

My brother Antoine has NEVER kissed me. Like, NOT ONCE. Incredible, right?

Personality: weird and annoying

My friends kiss me a lot. Eva always keeps her mouth slightly open, for example.

Mwah hha!

Personality: insecure about air — needs to breathe a lot

Cassandra stops moving completely when she kisses. It's the kissee (new word alert LOL) who ends the kiss, not her!

If I don't move away, she just stays like that

Personality: affectionate and maybe a little clingy

I don't really know how to analyse my kisses. I'd say that only my lips move and I never close my eyes.

Mwwah

What do you think?

(Based on a true story told by Esther A, who is 12 years old)

Riad Sattouf

Safety

I love feeling safe. And the place I feel the safest on earth is in my bed, under my covers. I curl up inside them, leaving just a little hole that I can breathe through. It's warm and cosy in my hiding place. I feel so good there and I imagine all sorts of harsh, freaky things happening outside that can't reach me (and that makes me even happier to be where I am)... For example:

A storm is blowing, rain pours down, the air is cold, and death prowls in a hostile landscape... ...but none of it touches me

A river of lava flows endlessly, wiping out all life... ...but my shelter is spared from the magma

I'm at the bottom of the ocean... ...in my bubble

I'm on a little platform at the top of a pylon that rises above the clouds, thousands of metres in the air... ...but my eyes are closed, so I don't get vertigo

I've gone billions of years back in time and I'm surrounded by vicious dinosaurs... ROARRr ...but my shelter keeps them away!

I'm on an ice floe and it's so cold that even the penguins are freezing... WOUUUUUUU ...but I'm perfectly warm (ha ha)

I'm on the moon, and everybody else is far, far away... ...and I feel fine

Now I just have to fall asleep (LOL)

(Based on a true story told by Esther A, who is 12 years old)

Riad Sattouf

Gaetan

You probably remember that I have a little brother. His name is Gaetan and he'll be 2 in November.

This is him and me in "perfect big sister" mode

I'm reading him a story

I like watching him grow up. It's very interesting to see all the things that make us different, even at such a young age.

... Kaki says "Whyyyy do I have to sleep?"

Gaetan.

HUH?

VVRRRTCHH

I'm trying to awaken his "feminine" side (sensitivity, gentleness, understanding) and believe me it's hard.

Gaetan, can you please stay focused? If you can't focus, you'll never get anywhere in life! I'M READING YOU A STORY HERE.

VRRCHH!

BIN LOWWY!

VVRRCHIIIVRRR

Total fascination →

A message to anyone who thinks that boys and girls are essentially the same: you are completely wrong and know nothing about life.

BIIIIN LOOOOWWY!

VVRRCHIIIIH!

Personally, I couldn't give a flying fuck about bin lorries... When I was a kid, it was all dolls and girly stuff.

I gave life to these plastic objects using my imagination

BAY-BEE

I had a Nenuco, I remember

So I knew from a very young age that I'd be a mother one day (I want four daughters).

I never got rid of it!

Gaetan! Come over here, we're going to look after the little baby. He needs his nappy changing and...

NO!

Gaetan will probably be a binman. You can't argue with destiny.

Bin lowwy

VRRCHHH!

We're born girls or boys, with our small similarities and our huge differences. Let's just try to get along!

"Come on Nenuco, let's drive this BIN LORRY"

vroum vroum

Bin lowwy?

NO!

And let's accept that this situation will never change.

La La La

(Based on a true story told by Esther A, who is 12 years old)

Riad Sattouf

51

Esther's Notebooks: the Film

Listen up, this is totally fresh yo! I recently found out that some film producers (very rich people who make and pay for films) were interested in turning the cartoon books of "Esther's Notebooks" into a film with real actors and everything!!! INCREDIBLE, right? But please <u>please</u> don't cast French actors because they're rubbish. You need to get Americans — they're way more talented. Okay? And whatever you do, you have to get adult actors to play all the roles, even us young ones, because it's easier to identify with them. So here are a few suggestions for the cast (well, you never know).

<u>My dad: Johnny Depp</u>
I like this actor because he's funny and good-looking (yep, just like my dad) and he even looks like him

Passionate and tender

<u>My mum: Gal Gadot</u>
She's the one who played Wonder Woman. A dynamic woman who's not afraid of going out in public without make-up, and who used to be a model

<u>My little brother:</u>
Just find a child model with a sweet angelic face (there aren't any 2-year-old celebrities)

The three boys fighting over me:
<u>Matthew Morrison:</u>
Looks good enough to eat (LOL)

<u>Antoine:</u>
<u>Nekfeu</u>
The only French guy in the cast (my brother's a huge fan so this is for him)

<u>Chace Crawford:</u> ♡

<u>Me:</u>
<u>Cara Delevingne</u>
Actress, model, melancholic... I adore her!

<u>My friend Eva:</u>
<u>Jayma Mays</u>
Sarcastic redhead, not too pretty

<u>An enemy:</u>
<u>Mercedes Lambre</u>
from "Violetta": She's beautiful and horrible at the same time

<u>Chris Pine:</u>
Casually bewitching, darkly handsome blond

<u>Not bad, huh?</u>

(Based on a true story told by Esther A, who is 12 years old)
Riad Sattouf

52

Nostalgia

Um, you might want to sit down for this. I'm going to tell you something that will probably shock you.

I LOVE THE FIRST DAY OF SCHOOL!

I like the ATMOSPHERE of this time of year.

I'm full of nostalgic thoughts, as if someone had their hand round my heart and was squeezing really hard.

I think about all the time that's gone past and will never come back, in "I'm getting older" mode...

... and about everything that might happen to me this year and also during the rest of my life.

I didn't go to summer camp this year (they were fully booked), so I stayed at my granny's house in Brittany.

I did my summer schoolwork – I love that!

I don't know what Year 8 will be like!

I'd really like to be the best student in my school to make my parents proud...

... without losing my reputation as someone adorably funny and likeable, of course!

I'd like to continue being loved by everybody

(Based on a true story told by Esther A, who is 12 years old)

Riad Sattouf

53

Year 8

Today was the first day of school — and it was very strange.

After that I vegged out at home (breakfast, TV, then a nap, as if I hadn't already slept enough).

My parents were at work, Antoine was at school, Gaetan was with his childminder...

I texted with Eva and we arranged to meet up outside the school at 2 p.m. ...

Around 11.30 I took a shower and as I stared at the tiles on the wall...

... I swear it really felt like I was a FROG.

After that, my mum suggested we eat lunch at a restaurant near the school.

The food was good but too peppery. My mouth was on fire.

I walked from the restaurant to my school and this really good-looking adult man smiled at me in the street.

Then we all stood in the school courtyard and the headmistress gave a really boring speech.

So here's something new: there are going to be two types of class representatives this year: "normal reps" and "green reps" who have to look after trees and tell the caretaker when the bins are full.

Nah I'm joking (LMFAO)

(Based on a true story told by Esther A, who is 12 years old)

Riad Sattouf

54

MISSED MY FIRST TWO BOOKS?

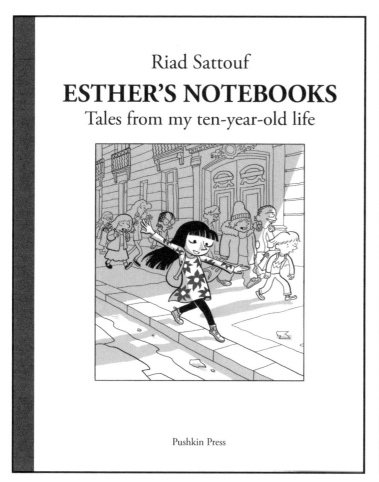

Riad Sattouf

ESTHER'S NOTEBOOKS

Tales from my ten-year-old life

Pushkin Press

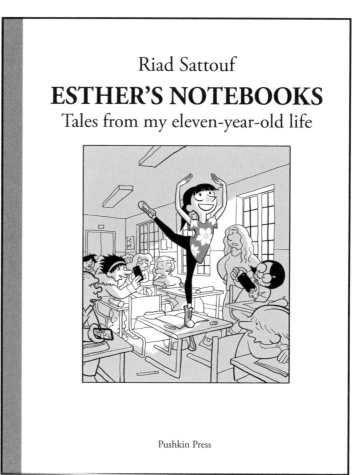

Riad Sattouf

ESTHER'S NOTEBOOKS

Tales from my eleven-year-old life

Pushkin Press

Pushkin Press
71–75 Shelton Street
London WC2H 9JQ

The graphic novel *Les cahiers d'Esther volume 3*
by Riad Sattouf was first published in French in 2017 by Allary Éditions.
© Allary Éditions and Riad Sattouf

English translation © Sam Taylor 2021

First published by Pushkin Press in 2021

These stories were pre-published in *L'Obs* between October 2016 and October 2017.

Thanks to Matthieu Croissandeau

INSTITUT
FRANÇAIS

This book is supported by the Institut français (Royaume-Uni) as part of the Burgess programme

1 3 5 7 9 8 6 4 2

ISBN 13: 978-1-78227-619-7

English version designed by Tetragon and Lucie Cohen

Printed and bound in Italy by Printer Trento SRL

www.pushkinpress.com

www.riadsattouf.com

 riadsattoufofficiel riadsattouf riadsattouf